Jip's book

Illustrated by Nina O'Connell

Nelson

A fish for tea

Jip has got a net.

"I will get a fish for tea,"
said Jip.

Jip put the net in
the water.
Will he get a fish?

What is in the net?

Has Jip got a fish?

It is a tin.

But what is in the tin?

"It is a fish,"
said Jip.
"I will have it for tea."

Up the tree

Jip ran up the tree.

He ran up to the top.

"I am up the tree,"
said Jip.
"Look at me."

8

"Can I get up the tree?"
said Meg the hen.
"No," said Jip.

"The tree is too big.
You can't get to the top,"
said Jip.

"I can," said Meg.

"I can fly.

I can fly to the top.

Look at me."

Can you swim?

"Look at me.

I can swim," said Ben.

"Come and swim with me, Jip."

"Go on, Jip," said Ben.

"Go on, Jip," said Sam.

"You can swim."

"No, no, no.

I can't swim," said Jip.

"Help, help.

I can't swim," said Jip.

"Help, help."

14

"I can help you,"
said Pat the pig.
"Are you wet?
Come home with me."

15

"Come and have tea,"
said Pat the pig.